Discover Writing Discover Korea 8

[여는 말]

한국에는 수준 높은 좋은 영어 교재들이 많이 있습니다. 그러나 이들 중 대부분의 책들은 한국 학생들의 삶과 문화에 진정으로 연결되어 있지 않고, 외국 문화와 맥락으로 가득 차 있습니다. 학생들이 교재의 내용에 공감하지 못해 영어에 대한 관심을 잃는 것을 보며 이러한 의문들이 들기 시작했습니다. "만약 한국 문화를 중심으로 한 교재가 있다면 어떨까?", "만약 교재가 학생들의 일상 생활과 더 밀접하게 연결되어 있다면 어떨까?".

이렇게 시작된 "만약"은 "나도 어쩌면 작은 변화를 가져올 수 있다."는 생각의 씨앗이 되었습니다. 모든 것을 바꿀 방법은 없을지도 모르지만, 제가 시작점이 되어 한국 학생들을 위한, 한국 문화를 반영한 영어 학습 자료, 그리고 학생들에게 친숙하고 위로가 되는 학습자료를 제공하고 싶었습니다.

Discover Writing Discover Korea 시리즈는 **총 10 권**으로 구성되어 있습니다. 이 시리즈는 제목에서도 선명하게 보이듯이 영어 글쓰기를 위한 책입니다. 이 10 권의 책시리즈들은 **각 장르별 영어 글쓰기 스킬을 제공**하면서 동시에 **다른 책에서 다루지 않는 문법의 일면들을 제공**하고 있습니다. 이 책을 통해 또한 **학생들은 자기평가가 가능**합니다. 보통의 교실환경에서 학생들은 주로 평가를 받는 입장입니다. 학생들은 점수에만 매인 채 평가의 의미와 결과의 이유는 잘 알지 못합니다. 이 책에서는 학습자가 평가의 주체가 되어 봄으로서 새로운 시각으로 본인의 글을 볼 수 있는 기회를 제공합니다. 학습자들은 **친숙한 한국문화**를 밑바탕으로 낯선 컨텐츠에 방해받지 않고 쓰기학습이라는 **본연의 목적에 충실**할 수 있도록 설계되었습니다.

저는 **진정한 영어 글쓰기를 위한 쓰기교육**을 학생들이 이 책과 함께 이루어 나가길 소망합니다. 학생들이 이 책에 빠져들며 영어 글쓰기 실력을 향상시키고 진정한 학습의 기쁨을 맛볼 수 있기를 진심으로 바랍니다.

이 책이 만들어지기까지 항상 용기를 주었던 나의 가족들, 학교 동기 선생님들, 교수님들, 친구들 그리고 나의 학생들과 학부형님 모두에게 감사 인사를 드리고 싶습니다.

나의 고민을 함께해주며 같이 울고 웃어준 나의 남편, 전화한통도 조심스러웠던 양가 부모님과 표지 제작에 많은 도움을 준 내 동생, 항상 용기를 주시고 나의 가치를 인정해 주셨던 성희선생님과 지선선생님, 그리고 소중한 오랜 인연 해정님, 멋진 코믹을 사용할 수 있게 기회를 열어 주신 PIXTON, 지금의 책이 있을 수 있게 열정적인 조언을 주셨던 정은영 교수님과 박혜옥 교수님, 그리고 누구보다 나의 발전에 불을 지피고 영감을 주며 지켜봐 주신 Chris 교수님께 special thanks 를 드리고 싶습니다.

2

[Prologue]

In Korea, there are many high-quality English textbooks available. However, most of these books are not genuinely connected to the lives and culture of Korean students; they are filled with foreign contexts and cultures. It saddened me to see students unable to relate to the content of these textbooks, causing them to lose interest in learning English. This raised questions in my mind: "What if there were materials centered around Korean culture?" "What if textbooks were closely linked to students' daily lives?"

These "what ifs" planted the seed of the thought, "Perhaps I can make a small change." While I may not be able to change everything, I wanted to be the starting point for providing English learning materials that reflect Korean culture and are familiar and comforting to students.

The "Discover Writing Discover Korea" series is comprised of a total of 10 volumes. As clearly indicated by its title, this series is a book for English writing. These ten volumes offer English **writing skills specific to various genres while also providing aspects of grammar not covered in other books.** Through this series, **students can also conduct self-evaluation**. In typical classroom environments, students are usually on the receiving end of evaluations. They are often bound to scores, not fully understanding the meaning of the evaluations or the reasons behind their results. This book gives learners the opportunity to become the evaluators themselves, allowing them to see their writing from a new perspective. The series is designed so that learners can remain true to the fundamental goal of writing education without being hindered by unfamiliar content, **based on the familiar backdrop of Korean culture.**

I hope that students embark on a journey of true English writing education with these books. I sincerely wish for them to immerse themselves in these books, improve their English writing skills, and experience the true joy of learning.

I would like to express my gratitude to my family, schoolmates, teachers, friends, and all my students and fellow educators who have always supported me in the creation of this book.

To my husband, who shared my concerns and laughed and cried with me, to my cautious parents who were always just a phone call away, to my younger sister who provided invaluable assistance in designing the cover, to Seonghee and Jisun, who always encouraged me and recognized my worth; to my precious long-time friend, Hae-jung; to PIXTON for opening the opportunity to use amazing comics, to Professor Eun-young Jeong and Professor Hye-ok Park, who provided passionate advice and most importantly, to Professor Chris Douloff, who has been a source of inspiration, guidance, and unwavering support in my personal growth—special thanks to you all.

ORGANIZATION OF THE BOOK

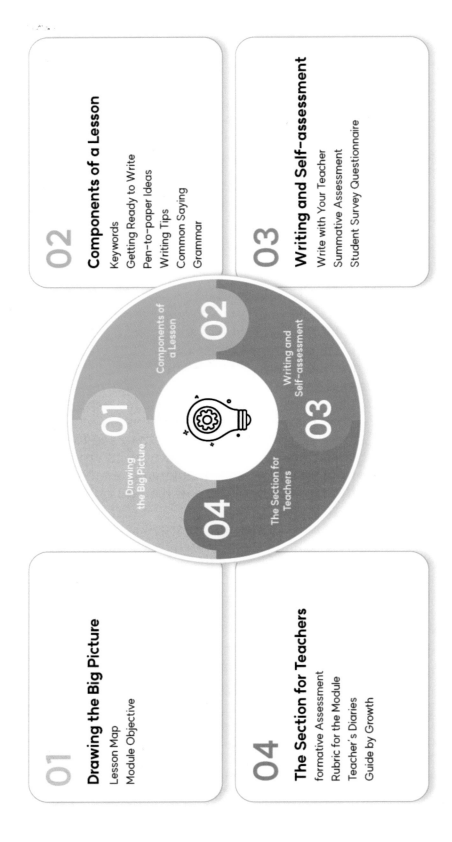

01 Drawing the Big Picture
Lesson Map
Module Objective

02 Components of a Lesson
Keywords
Getting Ready to Write
Pen-to-paper Ideas
Writing Tips
Common Saying
Grammar

03 Writing and Self-assessment
Write with Your Teacher
Summative Assessment
Student Survey Questionnaire

04 The Section for Teachers
formative Assessment
Rubric for the Module
Teacher's Diaries
Guide by Growth

INTRODUCTION OF TLC, GENRE WRITING, AND PROCESS WRITING

The teaching-learning cycle, genre writing, and process writing are three effective methods that interrelate and complement each other in fostering students' writing skills.

1. Teaching-Learning Cycle (TLC)

The Teaching-Learning Cycle is a systematic approach to teaching that involves four stages: **building the field** (contextualizing and building background knowledge), **modeling** (showcasing examples), **joint construction** (collaborative writing), and **independent construction** (students write on their own).

Relation to Other Methods: TLC acts as a framework where genre writing and process writing can be incorporated. For example, while modeling, you can introduce different genres and engage students in the process of writing stages.

Application: Start by engaging students with images or discussions to build context (**Building the Field**). Then, provide a well-structured example text (**Modelling**), followed by collaborative writing (**Joint Construction**). Finally, allow students to write independently.

2. Genre Writing

Genre writing focuses on teaching students about different text types or genres such as narratives, reports, or persuasive texts, and **the language features and structures commonly used** in each.

Relation to Other Methods: Within the TLC, different genres can be modeled and practiced. Process writing can be applied within a specific genre to go through the drafting, revising, and editing stages.

Application: Choose a **genre** and **model a text**, discussing its **specific language features** and **structures**. Then, **guide** students to write their own texts following the conventions of the chosen genre.

3. Process Writing

Process writing emphasizes the steps or processes in writing such as planning, drafting, revising, editing, and publishing.

Relation to Other Methods: It can be embedded within the TLC during the independent construction phase and can be utilized across different genres.

Application: Guide students through each stage, from brainstorming ideas (**Planning**), writing a first draft (**Drafting**), getting and giving feedback (**Revising**), correcting errors (**Editing**), to finally publishing their work.

The integration of these three methods offers a **comprehensive, structured, and student-centered approach to teaching writing**, which supports students in becoming autonomous, reflective, and proficient writers.

TABLE OF CONTENTS

LESSON MAP

MODULE 8: FORMAL EMAIL WRITING							
		GET READY TO WRITE			WRITE		REVISE & EDIT
	KEYWORDS	MODEL TEXTS	PEN-TO-PAPER IDEAS & WRITING TIPS	GRAMMAR	WRITE WITH YOUR TEACHER	WRITE BY YOURSELF	EDITING
	complete, response, assure, catch up, absence, assignment, inform, request, accompany, see off	PLEASE LET ME KNOW IF THERE IS ANY ASSIGNMENT OR WORK.	• create an appropriate subject. • apply how to request politely • recognize the differences between informal and formal lettering • Common Saying: *Please let me know if there…*	• politeness with past tense • past participle	• completing the unfinished part of a formal email	• challenge: write a formal email under the given prompts	• tense check

Example Lesson Plans: Module 1 [8 classes, 6 hours]

Module objectives ⭐2	*By the end of* **Module 1**, *a student will be better able to*
	O1. compose a self-introduction using simple, short sentences, and a first-person perspective considering the readership and purpose of the text. **O2.** understand language in chunks and fixed expressions **O3.** share personal information safely and appropriately, and use the appropriate tone. **O4.** apply simple vocabulary and present tense **O5.** understand the rules of the S-V agreement and apply them in writing.
Legend	TLC = Teaching learning cycle
Class 1	TLC stage: *Modelling*
Major Stages	**1.** Explain module objectives to S
	2. "Task A" (1–5): Have S read questions and discuss.
	3. "KEYWORDS": Have S check the target words and elicit their meaning. Help S pronounce words correctly. If needed, use **MORE EXERCISE FOR KEYWORDS**
	4. "Model Text": Have S read the given cartoon and understand the context. Give S a "Model Text" and encourage S to notice the target words in the text. Have S understand the content of the text using concept-checking questions (CCQ).
HW	**"HOMEWORK DAY 1"**
Class 2	TLC stage: *Modelling*
Major Stages	1. 1. **"HOMEWORK DAY 1":** to check + **"KEYWORDS":** to review + **"Model Text":** to review
	"**WRITING STRATEGIES**—"**Writing Process":** Have S read and discuss.
	1. **"DEEP DIVE":** Have S analyze **"Model Text"**. Have S consider the structure. S applies to **"DEEP DIVE A & B"**. If a learner doesn't have a partner, the teacher fills that role as a guide. Don't forget that the teacher's role is not only to teach but also to observe, and guide
HW	**"HOMEWORK DAY 2"**
Class 3	TLC stage: *Modelling*

Major Stages	1. **"HOMEWORK DAY 2"**: to check + **"KEYWORDS"**: to review + **"Model Text"**: to review
	2. **KEY ELEMENT & TIPS**—"Self-introduction Etiquette"(Tip 1–6): to check S understands tips for writing self-introduction. Have S complete **"EXERCISE 1, 2"**, **"HANDS-ON ACTIVITIES A, B"**, and **"DEEP DIVE A, B"**.
	3. **"SUMMARY"**: to review a letter-writing process
HW	**"HOMEWORK DAY 3"**
Class 4	TLC stage: *Modelling*
Major Stages	1. **"HOMEWORK DAY 3"**: to check + **"KEYWORDS"**: to review + **"Model Text"**: to review + **"Self-introduction Etiquette"(Tip1-6)**: to review
	2. **KEY ELEMENT & TIPS** —**Fixed Expression**: Have S read examples and elicit the expression's meaning. Have S solve **"EXERCISE 3–5"**.
	3. **"DEEP DIVE"**: Have S read **"Model Text"** and analyze the fixed expression in the text.
HW	**"HOMEWORK DAY 3"**
Class 5	TLC stage: *Modelling*
Major Stages	1. **"GRAMMAR 1"**: Have S think about when to use the present tense. Have S read **"GRAMMAR 1"** and provide some time to notice the function of the present tense. Have S solve **"EXERCISE 6"**. Conduct **CCQ**.
	2. **"DEEP DIVE A-D"**: Have S read "Model Text" and analyze.
	3. **"HANDS-ON ACTIVITIES A, B**: Have S solve.
HW	**"HOMEWORK DAY 5"**
Class 6	TLC stage: *Modelling*
Major Stages	1. "HOMEWORK DAY 5": to check + **"KEYWORDS"**: to review + **"Model Text"**: to review + **Self-introduction Etiquette (Tip1-6)** to review + **"Fixed Expression"**: to review + **"GRAMMAR 1"**: to review
	2. **"GRAMMAR 2-1"**: Have S think about the rule of present Be-verb. Have S read **"GRAMMAR 2-1"**. Have S solve **"EXERCISE 7"**. **Conduct CCQ.**
	2. **"GRAMMAR 2-2"**: Have S think about the rule of present Action-verb. Have S read **"GRAMMAR 2-2"**. Have S solve **"EXERCISE 8"**. **Conduct CCQ.**

	3. **"HANDS-ON ACTIVITIES"**: S makes sentences in "HANDS-ON ACTIVITIES A, B".
HW	**"HOMEWORK DAY 6"**
Class 7	TLC stage: *joint construction1–2*
Major Stages	1. **"HOMEWORK DAY 6"**: to check + **"KEYWORDS"**: to review + **"Model Text"**: to review + **Self-introduction Etiquette (Tip1-6)** to review + **"Fixed Expression"**: to review + **"GRAMMAR 1"**: to review "GRAMMAR 1": to review +**"GRAMMAR 2-1, 2-2"**: to review
	2. **"WRITE WITH YOUR TEACHER 1"**: Have S understand the purpose of the task. Guide S to complete the unfinished text. Demonstrate S how to revise and edit using the checklist.
	3. **"WRITE WITH YOUR TEACHER 2"**: Have S understand the task's purpose and demonstrate the process writing procedure. Complete the task with S.
HW	**"HOMEWORK DAY 7"**
Class 8	TLC stage: *Independent construction*
Major Stages	1. **"HOMEWORK DAY 7"**: to check + **"KEYWORDS"**: to review + **"Model Text"**: to review + **Self-introduction Etiquette (Tip1-6)** to review + **"Fixed Expression"**: to review + **"GRAMMAR 1"**: to review "GRAMMAR 1": to review +**"GRAMMAR 2-1, 2-2"**: to review + **"WRITE WITH YOUR TEACHER 2"**: to review the procedure of process writing
	2. **"INDEPENDENT WRITING"**: Have S understand the purpose of the task. Have S look through and complete the task.

MODULE OBJECTIVES

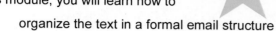

In this module, you will learn how to

- organize the text in a formal email structure

- apply how to request politely

- recognize the differences between informal and formal lettering

- create an appropriate subject

- understand the procedures of pre-writing, drafting, revising, and editing.

A.   Answer the questions. Discuss with your partner.
1. Have you read any formal emails? What kind of email was it?
2. Who sent you?
3. What did the writer want to say in the email?
4. Are Korean formal emails and English ones similar or different?

KEYWORDS

Match the words with pictures. Check the meanings and pronunciation with your teacher.

To finish his homework, Se-chan needed to _____ the last question.

▪

▪ assure

When the teacher asked a question, Tae-woo quickly raised his hand to give a _____.

▪

▪ inform

"For today's _____, please read chapter three of your science book," said my teacher.

▪

▪ complete

My dad will _____ me to my first day at the new school.

▪

▪ response

I'll need to _____ with the rest of the class by studying extra hours tonight.

▪

▪ catch up

Mom had to _____ my little brother that there were no monsters under his bed.

▪

▪ request

▪

▪ absence

▪

▪ accompany

▪

▪ assignment

▪

▪ see off

MORE EXERCISE FOR KEYWORDS

Exercise 1. Check the meaning of each word above again. Put them with the word that takes the same role in each box together. Work with your partner. Follow an example.

e.g., apple, bus, cat…	e.g., pretty, soft, big…	e.g., eat, have, run…

Exercise 2. Check the pronunciation and stress of each word. Work with your partner. Follow an example.

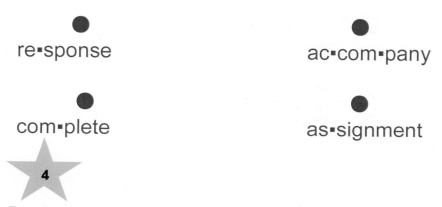

●
re▪sponse

●
ac▪com▪pany

●
com▪plete

●
as▪signment

★ **4**

Exercise 3. Look up the words again. Can you guess what story is in the text? Discuss with your partner.

MORE EXERCISE FOR KEYWORDS

Exercise 4. Fill in the gap with the words below.

> complete, response, absence, assignment, request. catch up, see off, assure, accompany, inform

1. Her mother agreed to _____ her on her first visit to the dentist.

2. The teacher was happy with Lisa's quick _____ to the difficult question.

3. Please _____ your parents about the change in the school schedule.

4. To _____ his model airplane, Kevin just needed to attach the wings.

5. The coach had to _____ the team that they could win the match.

6. The history teacher gave an _____ to write an essay about ancient Egypt.

7. The whole family went to the airport to _____ their grandmother who was traveling to Spain.

8. After being sick for a week, Mark had to _____ on all the lessons he missed.

9. Samantha made a _____ to the librarian to help her find a book about dinosaurs.

10. The classroom felt empty in the _____ of Mrs. Smith, the regular teacher.

11. We all gathered at the train station to _____ our friend who was leaving for college.

12. Our math _____ for tomorrow is to solve ten problems.

13. After the holiday, the students had to _____ on the chapters they missed.

14. During his _____, the team realized how important James was to their project.

15. The whole team came to _____ the coach who was moving to a different city.

MODULE 8 — WHAT SHALL I DO TO INFORM MY ABSENCE TO MY TEACHER?

Sally wants to go to the Kimpo airport with her grandmother to see her off. Sally is thinking about how and what to write her Korean language teacher.

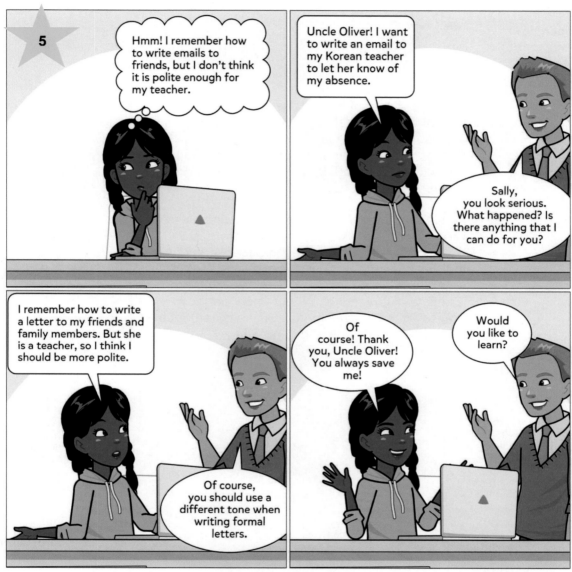

Comic made at Pixton.com

15

Model Text

subject

It immediately informs the reader about the main purpose or topic of the letter. It acts as a summary or a headline.

Subject: Request for Absence on December 8th

opening+ recipient(s)

This is the beginning of the letter where the writer greets the recipient. It addresses the person to whom the letter is written. Using a formal title and last name shows respect and formality.

Dear Ms. Yeom,

I am writing to inform you about my absence next week.

I was wondering if it would be possible for me to be absent from the Korean language class on December 8th. The reason for my request is that I need to accompany my grandmother to Kimpo Airport. She is traveling to Jeju and I would like to be there to see her off.

content

The letter follows a clear format – starting with the reason for writing, explaining the situation, and then politely asking for understanding or action. The sentences are polite and clearly state the purpose.

I understand the importance of attending class and I assure you that I will catch up on any missed work. I wanted to inform you in advance to ensure that my absence is not a surprise.

Thank you very much for your understanding. Please let me know if there is any assignment or work, I should complete beforehand.

Looking forward to your kind response.

closing

This is where the writer begins to end the letter. It concludes politely and professionally.

Sincerely,

Sally

sender

This is the name of the person who wrote the letter. It lets the recipient know who the letter is from.

Comic made at Pixton.com

Comic made at Pixton.com

What are Chains in Communication?

A chain is a way of showing who talks to whom in a group, like in a school or a company. It's like a map that shows who is in charge and who are the team members.

Why are they important?

▪ **Clear Roles:** These chains make it clear who should be talking to whom, which makes communication easier and more organized.

▪ **Understanding Expectations:** Each type of chain has its own expectations for how to talk and what kind of information to share. When you know this, it's easier to communicate effectively.

• **Efficiency:** By using these chains, messages and information get to the right people in the right way, which saves time and avoids confusion.

Comic made at Pixton.com

1. Up the Chain:

This is when you talk or write to someone who is in a higher position than you. It shows respect and understanding of authority. It's how you ask for help or permission from someone who can make decisions.

e.g., When you ask your teacher a question or write a letter to the school principal.

2. Across the Chain

This happens when you communicate with people who are at the same level as you. It helps in working together, sharing ideas, and making friendships. It's important for teamwork and getting along with others.

e.g., When talking to your classmates or friends.

3. Down the Chain

This is when someone in a higher position communicates with someone lower. It's how leaders or those in charge give instructions, information, or guidance.

e.g., When your teacher gives you homework or instructions.

DEEP DIVE

A.   Look at the model text. Then answer the questions.

1. What genre does the text belong to?

2. What is the purpose of the text?

3. How many parts are in the text? Can you explain the function of each part?

B.   Look at the model text. Then answer the questions.

1. Who was the reader of the text?

2. Who was the writer?

3. How close is the reader and the writer? How do you know it?

4. Find one example that shows the relationship between the reader and the writer from the model text.

C.   Fill in the blanks with the body parts. Read the letter below and circle the writer and reader. Then underline the purpose of this text.

Subject: Re: Request for Absence on December 8th   _____

Dear Sally,   _____

Thank you for informing me about your request to be absent from the Korean language class on December 8th.

I understand the importance of family commitments, and I appreciate that you took the time to notify me in advance about your need to accompany your grandmother to the airport. It's good to know that you are willing to help your family when needed.

Regarding your absence, it is granted for December 8th. I admire your responsibility in planning to catch up on any missed work. To help you with this, I will email you the class notes and any assignments we cover on that day. Additionally, please feel free to reach out to me or any of your classmates if you have questions or need further clarification on the material.

I hope your grandmother has a safe and pleasant trip to Jeju. We will miss you in class but look forward to having you back with us soon.

Thank you again for your thoughtful approach to handling your academic responsibilities while supporting your family.

_____

Best,   _____

Ms. Yeom   _____

Comic made at Pixton.com

| TIP 1 | SUBJECT |

The subject line is like a title for the email. It should give the reader a clear idea of what the email is about. Here's how you can explain it with examples:

• Keep it Short and Clear: The subject should be brief but descriptive enough to convey the main point of the email.
• Be Specific: Avoid vague subjects. The reader should know what to expect in the email.
• Purpose of the Email: Indicate if the email is for a request, an update, an invitation, etc.

7

Situation	Good example ✓	Bad example X
Asking for Homework Help	**Request** for Help with Math Homework Chapter 3	Question
Informing About Absence	**Absence** Notification for September 10th Due to Doctor's Appointment	School
Submitting a School Project	Science Project **Submission:** Volcano Model by Lisa	Project

EXERCISE 1. Read situation. Write appropriate subjects for each situation. Follow the example.

e.g., You need to tell your teacher that you will miss school next Friday for a family event.

→ Upcoming Absence on Friday for a family event

Situation 1. You're emailing to inform your teacher that you'll be late for school due to a doctor's appointment.

→ _____

Situation 2. You have a question about the homework for your math class.

→ _____

Situation 3. You are emailing your teacher about a lost item you think you left in their classroom.

→ _____

TIP2	HOW TO WRITE REASONS

1. Start with a Clear Purpose: Begin your letter by clearly stating why you are writing. This helps the reader understand the context right away.

2. Be Specific: Provide specific details about your reason. Avoid being too vague.

3. Keep it Brief: At the A1 level, it's important to keep the language simple and to the point. Long, complicated sentences can be confusing.

4. Use Polite Language: Even when stating a reason, it's important to be polite. Use phrases like *I would like to, I am hoping to,* or *I am writing to request.*

e.g., I am writing to request permission for a leave of absence on November 17th.
e.g., I need to be absent because I have a medical appointment.
e.g., I understand that missing this day means I will miss the math test, and I am willing to take it on another date.

8

EXERCISE 2. Read situation. Write appropriate reasons for each situation. Follow the example.

e.g., You need to tell your teacher that you will miss school next Friday for a family trip.

→ I am writing to request a day off next Friday for a family trip.

Situation 1. You're emailing to inform your teacher that you'll be late for school due to a doctor's appointment.

→ _____

_____

Situation 2. You have a question about the homework for your math class.

→ _____

_____

Situation 3. You are emailing your teacher about a lost item you think you left in their classroom.

→ _____

_____

TIP3	HOW TO ADD DETAILS IN CONTENTS

1. Be Specific: Include specific information that relates to your reason. Avoid general statements.

2. Use Simple Language: Keep your sentences short and easy to understand.

3. Stay on Topic: Make sure all the details you add are related to the main reason you're writing the letter.

4. Organize Your Thoughts: Present your details in a logical order. It can be helpful to write down your points before you start the letter.

5. Be Honest and Accurate: Ensure that the details you provide are true and accurate.

EXERCISE 3. Read situation. Write appropriate details for each situation. Follow the example.

e.g., You need to tell your teacher that you will miss school next Friday for a family event.
Subject: Upcoming Absence on Friday for a family event
Reason: I am writing to request a day off next Friday for a family event.
Details: This event is my cousin's wedding. It will take place in Busan. It is important for me to be there with my family. I will leave school next Friday and return on Sunday.

Situation 1. You are emailing to inform your teacher that you'll be late for school due to a doctor's appointment.
Subject: Informing of Late Arrival Due to Doctor's Appointment on December 15th.
Reason: I have a doctor's appointment on December 15th in the morning, so I will not be able to arrive at school on time.
Details: _____

_____

Situation 2. You have a question about the homework for your math class.
Subject: Question Regarding Math Homework for Thursday Class
Reason: I am having trouble understanding the homework for our math class on Thursday.
Details: _____

_____

Situation 3. You are emailing your teacher about a lost item you think you left in their classroom.
Subject: Lost item in class
Reason: I believe I left my water bottle in our classroom yesterday.
Details: _____

_____

TIP4	EXPLAIN THE EFFECT OF YOUR SITUATION ON THE RECIPIENT

1. Understand You Better: If you explain why you're writing and how it touches their life, the person reading your letter or email can understand you better.

2. Clearer Message: It helps them know why you're telling them this and what's important about it.

3. Solve Problems: If the person knows how your situation affects them, they can think of better ways to help or fix any problems. Like, if you tell your teacher you'll miss class, they can plan how to help you catch up.

4. Build Friendship: It shows you care about them, not just what you need.

EXERCISE 4. Read situation. Write appropriate effects for each situation. Follow the example.

e.g., You need to tell your teacher that you will miss school next Friday for a family event.
Subject: Upcoming Absence on Friday for a family event
Reason: I am writing to request a day off next Friday for a family event.
Details: This event is my cousin's wedding. It will take place in Busan. It is important for me to be there with my family. I will leave school next Friday and return on Sunday.
Effect: This means I will miss the lessons you will teach next Friday. I know we might have important classes or activities that day. I am sorry for any trouble this might cause.

Situation 1. You're emailing to inform your teacher that you'll be late for school due to a doctor's appointment.
Subject: Informing of Late Arrival Due to Doctor's Appointment on December 15th.
Reason: I have a doctor's appointment on December 15th in the morning, so I will not be able to arrive at school on time.
Details: The appointment is at 8:30 AM and it may take around one hour. I plan to reach school by 10:00 AM.
Effect:

_____

Situation 2. You have a question about the homework for your math class.
Subject: Question Regarding Math Homework for Thursday Class
Reason: I am having trouble understanding the homework for our math class on Thursday.
Details: I am stuck on the problems related to algebraic equations. I tried to solve them but couldn't understand how to find the correct answers.
Effect:

_____

Situation 3. You are emailing your teacher about a lost item you think you left in their classroom.
Subject: Lost item in class
Reason: I believe I left my water bottle in our classroom yesterday.
Details: It's a blue water bottle with stickers on it. I always keep it on my desk during class. I think I forgot to put it back in my bag before leaving.
Effect:

_____

TIP5   SOLUTION

1. Shows You Care: When you add a solution in your letter, it shows you care about fixing any problems.

2. Helps Fix Things: Your solution can help fix the problem you're talking about. **9**

3. Makes It Easier for Others: When you give a solution, it makes it easier for the person reading your letter.

4. Shows Respect: It shows you respect the person you're writing to because you're thinking about how your actions affect them.

5. Builds Trust: When you often include solutions in your letters, people start to trust you.

EXERCISE 5. Read situation. Write appropriate solutions for each situation. Follow the example.

e.g., Subject: Upcoming Absence on Friday for a family event
Reason: I am writing to request a day off next Friday for a family event.
Details: This event is my cousin's wedding. It will take place in Busan. It is important for me to be there with my family. I will leave school next Friday and return on Sunday.
Effect: This means I will miss the lessons you will teach next Friday. I know we might have important classes or activities that day. I am sorry for any trouble this might cause.
Solution: I will make sure to ask my friends about what I miss and do any homework over the weekend so I can catch up quickly when I return to school on Monday.

---

1. Subject: Informing of Late Arrival Due to Doctor's Appointment on December 15th.
Reason: I have a doctor's appointment on December 15th in the morning, so I will not be able to arrive at school on time.
Details: The appointment is at 8:30 AM and it may take around one hour. I plan to reach school by 10:00 AM.
Effect: I will miss some class time. This might mean you have to help me catch up later. I'm sorry for the extra work.
Solution:

---

2. Subject: Question Regarding Math Homework for Thursday Class
Reason: I am having trouble understanding the homework for our math class on Thursday.
Details: I am stuck on the problems related to algebraic equations. I tried to solve them but couldn't understand how to find the correct answers.
Effect: If I don't get help, I might not understand our next math lesson. This could make it harder for me in class.
Solution:

---

3. Subject: Lost item in class
Reason: I believe I left my water bottle in our classroom yesterday.
Details: It's a blue water bottle with stickers on it. I always keep it on my desk during class. I think I forgot to put it back in my bag before leaving.
Effect: If you find my water bottle, you'll need to keep it until I can get it. I know this is extra work for you. Thank you for helping.
Solution:

MORE EXERCISE FOR REASONING, EFFECT AND SOLUTION

EXERCISE 1. Read the story. Fill the blank considering **TIP 1–5**.

Text A

Last weekend, I was riding my bike near my house. It was fun until I had to suddenly swerve to avoid hitting a small dog. I lost control and fell off my bike. It hurt a lot, and I couldn't stand up.

My neighbor saw me fall and called my parents. They took me to the hospital, and the doctor said I broke my ankle. Now, I have a cast and need to rest for a week, so I can't come to school.

I'm worried about missing classes and falling behind. I need to write a letter to my teacher to tell them about my accident, explain why I can't come to school, and ask for help with keeping up with my schoolwork from home.

Subject
:_____

Reason
:_____

Detail
:_____

Effect
:_____

Solution
:_____

Tip6   Closing

When you finish a formal letter, the way you say goodbye is important. It shows you are polite and serious.

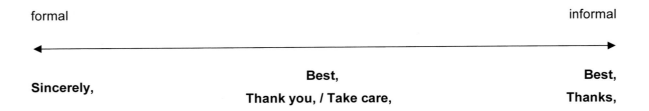

formal   informal

Sincerely,

Best,
Thank you, / Take care,

Best,
Thanks,

DEEP DIVE

A. Read the letter below. Compare it with the Model Text. Then find five mistakes and correct them. Work with your partner.

Subject: Lost

Hi, Ms. Yeom

I believe I left my water bottle in our classroom yesterday. If you do find my water bottle, could you please keep it in a safe place? Maybe it could be kept in your office or the lost and found area. I will come to pick it up as soon as I am back in school.
It's a blue water bottle with stickers on it. I always keep it on my desk during class. I think I forgot to put it back in my bag before leaving. If it's not found, please let me know, and I'll check other places it might be.
Thank you so much for your help with this.

Thanks,
Tom

B. Read the Model Text. Underline **Tip1–6** in the text.

SUMMARY   FORMAL EMAIL

A formal writing process: (1) **Start with a subject** line that clearly tells what your email is about. It should be short and to the point. (2) **Begin with a polite greeting**, like "Dear [Name]". (3) In the first sentence or two, **explain why** you are writing the email. This is your reason or purpose for contacting the person. (4) **Give more information** about your reason. Keep it simple and clear. Stick to the main points that the reader needs to know. (5) **End with a polite closing**, like "Sincerely" followed by your name.

Subject	{ *Subject:*	
Greeting	{ *Dear the recipient's name*	
	{ *Reason + Details*	}
	{ *Solution*	**Content**
Closing	{ *Sincerely,*	
Sender's name	{ *Sender's name*	

A Few Days Later at the Airport

Comic made at Pixton.com

Comic made at Pixton.com

Please let me know if you can come to my birthday party.

Please let me know if you need any help with your homework.

People use **_please let me know_** when they want to find out something or need an answer from someone else. **_Please let me know_** is a polite way to ask someone to give you information or tell you something later. It's like saying, "Can you tell me?" or "I would like to know," It's a nice way to ask for the information you need.

Please let me know is often followed by introducing a clause with **_if_** or a question word like **_what, where, when, who, why,_** or **_how._**

e.g., **_Please let me know_** <u>if</u> you are coming to the party.

e.g., **_Please let me know_** <u>what time</u> the meeting starts.

EXERCISE 7. Read the given situations. Write your own sentences with **_please let me know..._** Follow the example.

Situation	
e.g., You need to know the due date of your English assignment.	e.g., Please let me know when the English assignment is due.
1. You want to find out if your friend is going to join the school trip.	→
2. You want to know what time the school library closes.	→
3. You're unsure about which book to read for your book report.he understands math now.	→

32

EXERCISE 8. Read the situations and write your own sentences to complete them. Follow the example.

e.g., You want to know the schedule for Seollal (Lunar New Year) school holiday.
What will you say?

→ Please let me know when our Seollal holiday starts and ends..

1. You want to know the time for a Taekwondo class.

What will you say?

→_____

2. You're curious about the lunch menu for the school's Korean New Year celebration.

What will you say?

→_____

3. You're asking about the meeting place for a group visit to Gyeongbokgung Palace.

What will you say?

→_____

EXERCISE 9. Write your own sentences using *please let me know...*.

1._____

2._____

3._____

4._____

DEEP DIVE

A. Read the Model Text again. Why did the writer say *please let me know...*? Discuss with your partner.

PAST TENSE AND POLITENESS

Comic made at Pixton.com

11

Why Use Past Tense for Politeness?

In English, using past tense verbs like "did" or "could" is a way to be polite and show respect, especially when asking questions or making requests.

1. Softening the Statement: When you use the past tense, it can make what you say sound less direct and softer. It's like you're not pushing someone to do something right now.

2. Showing Respect: By using the past tense, you're showing that you respect the other person's choice or decision.

e.g., What *is* your name?
e.g., What *was* your name?

In the second example, using past verbs makes the question sound more polite.

e.g., *Can* you help me with my homework?
e.g., *Could* you help me with my homework?

Could is the past tense of *Can*. it sounds more respectful and less demanding.

There are other past verb form that show respect and politeness.

e.g., I was wondering if…
e.g., I hoped…
e.g., I wanted…

cf. General expression vs. more polite expression

General expression	More polite expressions
I want	I would like I hoped I wanted
Thank you for (noun form)	I appreciate (noun form)
I'm sorry for (noun form)	I apologize for (noun form)
I'm curious about (noun form) I'm curious if (sentence form)	I was wondering if (sentence form)

EXERCISE 11. Look at the picture and make question or request sentences. Follow the examples.

1.	e.g., Could I help you to carry the bags? e.g., I wanted to help you to carry the bags.	Situation 1: You want to help to carry heavy stuff.	e.g., Can I help you to carry the bags? e.g., I want to help you to carry the bags.
2.	→ →	Situation 2: You want him to open the box for you.	→ →
3.	→ →	Situation 3: You want to explain how to use the robot.	→ →

EXERCISE 12. Read the Model text. Find past verbs. Group them in the box below. Think why the writer uses past verbs in the sentences. Work with your partner.

To express the time	To show respect and politeness

DEEP DIVE

A. When we see the past verb in the sentence, is it possible to guess the function of it at a glance? Discuss with your partner.

MORE EXERCISE FOR GRAMMAR1

Exercise 1. Read the situations and make requested sentences with politeness.

You want to inform your teacher that you will be absent today because you have got flu.

→ _____

You want your friend to open the window.

→ _____

You want to know how to get the museum, and now ask a stranger on the street.

→ _____

You are writing an email to her friend. You want your book back.

→ _____

You are writing an email to your grandfather. You want him to help you to make chairs with wood.

→ _____

You are curious if your mom can help you to bake for your father's birthday party.

→ _____

Regular Verbs Chart

Present Form	Past Form	Past Participle Form
walk	walked	walked
play	played	played
watch	watched	watched
clean	cleaned	cleaned
talk	talked	talked
cook	cooked	cooked
listen	listened	listened
jump	jumped	jumped
laugh	laughed	laughed
call	called	called

▪ **Past Form and Past Participle:** Notice that the past form and the past participle form are the same for regular verbs.

▪ **_-ed_ Ending:** In most cases, add _-ed_ to the base form to get both the past and past participle forms.

Remember past participles do not work as verbs.

e.g., She wore a _wrinkled_ shirt to school today.
e.g., The _boiled_ water is too hot to touch.

EXERCISE 17. Fill the the chart and put the past participle in the right place. Follow the example.

e.g.,

Present form	Past form	Past participle form
paint	painted	painted

The (**painted**) fence (   ) looks (   ) very (   ) colorful.

1.

Present form	Past form	Past participle form
close		

We (   ) saw (   ) a (   ) store (   ) on the (   ) way to (   )
school.

2.

Present form	Past form	Past participle form
wash		

She (   ) wore (   ) a (   ) dress (   ) to the (   ) party.

3.

Present form	Past form	Past participle form
drop		

She (   ) found (   ) a (   ) coin (   ) under the (   ) table.

Irregular Verbs Chart

Present Form	Past Form	Past Participle Form
be	was/were	been
break	broke	broken
choose	chose	chosen
cut	cut	cut
do	did	done
eat	ate	eaten
freeze	froze	frozen
fall	fell	fallen
throw	threw	thrown
steal	stole	stolen

▪ **Different Forms:** Notice that for irregular verbs, the past and past participle forms are often different from each other and from the base form.

▪ **No Specific Rule:** Irregular verbs do not follow a specific pattern, so their forms need to be memorized.

▪ **Common Verbs:** These are some of the more common irregular verbs, but there are many more.

Remember past participles do not work as verbs.

e.g., The _chosen_ book was her favorite.
e.g., The _frozen_ lake was beautiful in the sunlight.

EXERCISE 18. Fill the chart and put the past participle in the right place. Follow the example.

e.g.,

Present form	Past form	Past participle form
fall	fell	fallen

Mi-so (   ) found (   ) a (◄   ) leaf (   ) on the (   ) a ground.

1.

Present form	Past form	Past participle form
steal		

The (   ) bicycle (   ) was (   ) finally (   ) found.

2.

Present form	Past form	Past participle form
break		

The (   ) toy (   ) was (   ) in the (   ) corner."
3.

Present form	Past form	Past participle form
throw		

The (   ) ball (   ) broke (   ) the (   ) window.

MORE EXERCISE FOR GRAMMAR2

EXERCISE 1. Read the chart. Fill the blank with the appropriate form of the verb.

Present form	Past form	Past Participle form
look	looked	looked
print	printed	printed
lock	locked	locked
wash	washed	washed
plant	planted	planted
damage	damaged	damaged
watch	watched	watched
be	was/were	been
lose	lost	lost
write	wrote	written
choose	chose	chosen
read	read	read
find	found	found
wear	wore	worn
tear	tore	torn

1. So-hyen (   ) a (   ) dress to the party.

2. The (   ) flowers in the garden are blooming.

3. So-ra (   ) at the (   ) picture on the wall.

4. Su-mi (   ) a (   ) story in her book.

5. He-yeon (   ) a (   ) door at the end of the hallway.

6. Ha-rang (   ) a (   ) kitten under the porch.

7. Tae-won and Hyo-ri (   ) a flying bird disappears into the sky.

8. The (   ) clothes are now clean and dry.

9. Ji-sol (   ) the (   ) toy car.

10. The (   ) note was hard to read.

EXERCISE 2. Look at the picture. Match the right past participle with the picture. Write phrases with the past participle. Follow the example.

Picture			Present form	Past form	Past participle form
Phrase: The frozen lake		•	bite	bit	bitten
Phrase:	•	•	break	broke	broken
Phrase:	•	▼	freeze	froze	frozen
Phrase:	•	•	tear	tore	torn

DEEP DIVE

A. When do people use *past participle* in sentences? Discuss with your partner.

B. What past participle is used in the Model text? What is the advantage of using *past participle* in the sentences? Discuss with your partner.

HANDS-ON ACTIVITIES

A. Look at the picture. Write sentences using given words. Follow the example.

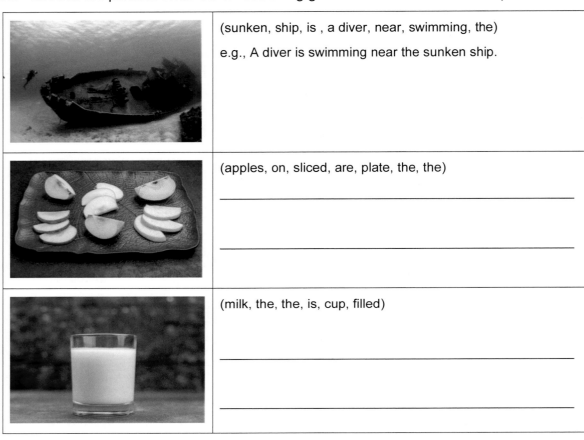

	(sunken, ship, is , a diver, near, swimming, the) e.g., A diver is swimming near the sunken ship.
	(apples, on, sliced, are, plate, the, the) _____ _____
	(milk, the, the, is, cup, filled) _____ _____

B. Write your own sentences with *past participle.* Work with your partner.

1._____

2._____

3._____

[CLASS7] WRITE WITH YOUR TEACHER 1	The purpose of this task is for you to practice formal email writing.

You are writing an email to your science teacher to inform him that you will miss his class next Tuesday because it is your great-grandmother's 80th birthday on that day.

Write a formal email that should include

• subject,

• who you are,

• why you are writing the email,

• what would happen to your teacher and you,

• what you would do to solve it, and

• use *please let me know* appropriately.

• use *past participles as adjectives* appropriately.

GAPS

Genre:		Purpose:	
Audience:		Style:	

WRITE

_____   _____

I am writing this email to _____

_____   _____ because _____

_____I know _____

_____   _____I will do _____

_____   _____

_____   _____

_____   _____

CHECKLIST

• Did I use the appropriate formal opening and closing? _____

• Did I use the appropriate formal letter structure? _____

• Did I keep English Letter Etiquette appropriately? _____

• Did I use *past participles* as adjectives? _____

• Did I use *please let me know-* appropriately? _____

• Did I understand the procedures of pre-writing, drafting, revising, and editing? _____

WRITE WITH YOUR TEACHER 2	The purpose of this task is for you to practice formal email writing.

You are writing an email to your school principal to request a new crosswalk at the front gate of your school.

Write a formal email that should include

• subject,

• who you are,

• why you are writing the email,

• what would happen to your teacher and you,

• what you would do to solve it, and

• use *please let me know* appropriately.

• use *past participles as adjectives* appropriately.

GAPS

Genre:		Audience:	
Purpose:		Style:	

PREWRITING

DRAFT

FINAL DRAFT

CHECKLIST

- Did I use the appropriate formal opening and closing? _____
- Did I use the appropriate formal letter structure? _____
- Did I keep English Letter Etiquette appropriately? _____
- Did I use *past participles* as adjectives? _____
- Did I use *please let me know-* appropriately? _____
- Did I understand the procedures of pre-writing, drafting, revising, and editing? _____

Formative Assessment: HOMEWORK

HOMEWORK DAY 1	KEYWORDS

1. Fill in the blanks with the words in the box below. You might need to change the form of the words (*e.g., play > playing, plays, or played*). The words might be used more than once or they might not be used at all.

complete, response, assure, catch up, absence, assignment, inform, request, accompany, see off

Subject: Request for Alternative P.E. Activity

Dear Mr. Lee,

I hope this email finds you well. I am writing to _____ you about a situation I am currently facing. Recently, I had a small accident and ended up with a broken finger. Due to this, I am unable to participate in our regular badminton activities in P.E.

I have always enjoyed P.E. classes and I _____ you that I am eager to stay active and engaged. However, with my current condition, _____ with badminton is quite challenging. Therefore, I kindly request if it would be possible to arrange an alternative activity that I can participate in during our P.E. sessions.

I understand that this might require extra planning on your part, and I truly appreciate your understanding and support in this matter. Please let me know if there are any _____ or tasks I can _____ as part of the alternative activity.

Thank you very much for considering my request. I look forward to your _____ and any suggestions you might have.

Sincerely,

Se-yoon

1. Fill in the blanks with the words in the box below. You might need to change the form of the words (*e.g., play > playing, plays, or played*). The words might be used more than once or they might not be used at all.

> complete, response, assure, catch up, absence, assignment, inform, request, accompany, see off

Subject: Apology for Missing the Scheduled Extra Math Class

Dear Ms. Seo,

I am writing to _____ you about a situation that has come up and to offer my sincere apologies.

Unfortunately, I will not be able to attend our scheduled extra math class tomorrow. The reason is, I have to _____ my cousin to the airport to ____ him ____. He is returning to the U.S., and my mom cannot take him because of her work. I _____ you that this situation was unexpected and I had hoped to _____ on our math _____ during the extra class.

To _____ our _____ and not fall behind, I will request the class notes from a classmate and study them thoroughly. Also, I would appreciate it if you could let me know if there are any additional resources or tasks I can do to make up for my_____.

I am truly sorry for any inconvenience this may cause and I _____ you it was not my intention.

Thank you for your understanding and support.

Sincerely,
Joo-ri Lim

2. Write about the structure of the formal emails.

3. Write about the types of chains and importance of them in emailing.

4. Read and find the GAPS of the given text. Then complete the table below.

Genre:	Audience:
Purpose:	Style:

Subject: Re: Apology for Missing the Scheduled Extra Math Class

Dear Joo-ri,

Thank you for your email and for letting me know about your situation. I understand that sometimes unexpected things happen, and family responsibilities are important.

I appreciate your proactive approach to catch up with the class work. It's a good idea to get the notes from your classmate. Additionally, I will send you a summary of the key points we cover in the extra class, along with a couple of practice problems. This should help you complete the assignment and stay on track.

Please do not worry about the class you will miss. If you have any questions or need further assistance once you've reviewed the notes and summary, feel free to reach out to me. We can arrange a time to discuss any topics you find challenging.

Thank you again for your responsible attitude and for informing me in advance. Safe travels to the airport and I look forward to seeing you back in class soon.

Best,

Ms. Seo

1. Fill in the blanks with the words in the box below. You might need to change the form of the words (*e.g., play > playing, plays, or played*). The words might be used more than once or they might not be used at all.

complete, response, assure, catch up, absence, assignment, inform, request, accompany, see off

Subject: Thank You and Request for Additional Help with Korean Class

Dear Jin-seo,

I hope you are doing well. I am writing to let you know how much I appreciate your help when I was absent from Korean class due to the flu.

Your notes were very helpful, and I am grateful that you _____ me about the _____ we received. It made it much easier for me to _____ with what I missed. I _____ you that your support made a big difference.

However, I am still trying to _____ the _____ and understand some of the topics we covered. If it's not too much trouble, could I _____ your help once more? Maybe you could explain some of the points I find difficult. I will prepare specific questions to make it easier.

Please let me know if you are available to help and when it would be convenient for you. I want to make sure I fully understand everything before our next class.

Thank you again for everything. Your kindness and assistance mean a lot to me.

Best,

Hyen-young

2. Write about 6 tips for writing a formal email.

3. Read and circle the mistakes. Then correct them. If needed, you can research.

Subject: Re: Thank You and Request for Additional Help with Korean Class

To. Hyun-young

I am free after school on Monday and Wednesday this week. Let me know which day works best for you, and we can meet in the library or anywhere you feel comfortable. Feel free to bring all your questions, and we can go through them together.

I'm so glad to hear from you and I'm happy that my notes and information about the assignments were helpful! It's no problem at all – I'm here to support you.

Don't worry, we'll make sure you understand everything clearly. Thank you for reaching out, and I'm looking forward to helping you.

See you soon!

Regarding your request for further help, of course, I would be happy to assist you. I can help you complete the assignments and explain the topics that are difficult for you. Let's make sure you catch up completely with the class.

From

Jin-seo.

1. Fill in the blanks with the words in the box below. You might need to change the form of the words (*e.g., play > playing, plays, or played*). The words might be used more than once or they might not be used at all.

> complete, response, assure, catch up, absence, assignment, inform, request, accompany, see off, please let me know

Subject: Questions About Science _____ on Plant Parts

Dear Mr. Park,

I am writing to _____ some help with our recent science _____. Unfortunately, I was absent from class last week due to illness.

My friend _____ me about the _____ on the parts of a plant, and I have been trying to _____ with the class. However, I have some questions about how fruits are produced. I _____ you that I have tried to find the answers myself, but I think I need a bit more explanation.

Could you please help me understand this topic better? I am especially confused about the process that leads from flowers to fruits. If you could provide a brief explanation or direct me to some resources, I would be very grateful.

_____ when you have some time to discuss this, or if you could answer my questions via email, that would also be very helpful.

Thank you for your understanding and assistance. I am looking forward to _____ this a_____ with a clear understanding of the topic.

Sincerely,

A-young

2. When can we use *please let me know* -.? Give one example that the expression can be used.

3. Read the situation use *please let me know* to complete sentences.

Situation 1: You want to borrow 'Harry Potter' from the school library but are not sure if it's available. You ask the librarian.

_____.

Situation 2: You want to join the school's art club but don't know when they meet. You ask a club member.

_____.

Situation 3: You want to know if the science project is a group assignment. You ask your science teacher by email.

_____.

Situation 4: You want to find out what you need to bring for the class picnic. You ask your teacher.

_____.

Situation 5: You want to know if there is homework in math class as you were absent yesterday. You ask your classmate.

_____.

1. Fill in the blanks with the words in the box below. You might need to change the form of the words (*e.g., play > playing, plays, or played*). The words might be used more than once or they might not be used at all.

complete, response, assure, catch up, absence, assignment, inform, request, accompany, see off, please let me know

Subject: Re: Questions About Science _____ on Plant Parts

Dear Kwang-hyen,

Thank you for reaching out and I hope you are feeling better now. It's great to see your eagerness to understand the science _____t despite your _____.

About your question on how fruits are produced from flowers: This process is known as pollination and fruit development. In simple terms, pollination is when pollen from one flower reaches the part of another flower that can produce seeds. After pollination, the fertilized flower starts to change and grow into a fruit, which contains the seeds.

To help you further, I've attached a few easy-to-understand resources and videos that explain this process. These should give you a clear picture of how flowers turn into fruits. Also, feel free to come by my office during lunch break if you need more explanation—I'd be happy to help!

_____ if you have more questions or need additional help after going through these resources. It's important to me that you understand and _____ your _____ confidently.

Take care and see you in class!

Best,

Mr. Park

2. Write about the function of the *past tense*.

3. Read the sentences. Change the sentences to show respect and more politeness. Follow the examples.

e.g., I want the shirt. I want to try it.
→ Could I try on this shirt?
→I was wondering if it is fine to try on this shirt.
→I wanted to try on this shirt.

1. I want to know the person's name.
→

2. I want to know if you can help me.
→

3. I hope you can come to my party.
→

4. I want to know when you can call me back.
→

5. I am curious if you can let me know what the math assignments are.
→

1. Fill in the blanks with the words in the box below. You might need to change the form of the words (*e.g., play > playing, plays, or played*). The words might be used more than once or they might not be used at all.   .

complete, response, assure, catch up, absence, assignment, inform, request, accompany, see off, please let me know

Subject: Apology for Missing the Art Museum Field Trip

Dear Mr. Jung,

I wanted to write to you about missing the field trip to the art museum last week.

Unfortunately, I had a family event that I couldn't miss, so I was absent from school that day. Because of this, I didn't know that we were supposed to choose an impressive artwork and submit a report about it.

I'm really sorry for missing the field trip and not _____ the _____. I _____ you it wasn't intentional. If there's any way I can _____ on this _____ or if you could _____ me about the details of the art piece I should write about, I would greatly appreciate it.

I'm eager to see off my report and make up for missing the field trip.

Once again, I apologize for my _____ and any inconvenience it may have caused. Thank you for your understanding.

Sincerely,

Eun-soo

2. Write about how past participles work in the sentences.

3. Read the email. Circle the past tense that functions to show politeness. Underline past verbs that functions to show the event happened in the past.

Subject: Apology for the Wet Book

Dear Ms. Choi,

I wanted to write to you to say how sorry I am for what happened to the book I borrowed from you.

Last week, I borrowed the novel from you, and I was really enjoying reading it. However, something unfortunate happened. I accidentally spilled water on the book, and it got completely wet. I didn't mean for this to happen, and I feel really bad about it.

To make things right, I would like to buy the same novel for you as a replacement. I know that it was my responsibility to take care of the book, and I want to make sure you have a new one to replace the damaged one. Please let me know if this would be okay with you. I can go to the bookstore and get the same book for you as soon as possible.

Once again, I am truly sorry for the mistake, and I hope you can forgive me. Please let me know if there's anything else I can do to make up for this. Thank you for your understanding.

Sincerely,

Na-rin

1. Fill in the blanks with the words in the box below. You might need to change the form of the words (*e.g., play > playing, plays, or played*). The words might be used more than once or they might not be used at all.

complete, response, assure, catch up, absence, assignment, inform, request, accompany, see off, please let me know

Subject: Apology and _____ for _____ Deadline Extension

Dear Ms.Kwon,

I am writing to apologize for the confusion regarding the submission date of our social studies assignment.

I got mixed up with the deadline, and I couldn't _____ the _____ on time. I am truly sorry for this mistake.

Is there any way you could please extend the deadline for me? I _____ you that I will _____ the _____ as soon as possible if you can give me a little extra time. Your understanding and support would be greatly appreciated.

Thank you for considering my _____. I will make sure to _____ you promptly once I _____ the _____.

Sincerely,

Hye-rin

2. You are writing an email to your school librarian to request a new set of books named 'Why?'

Write a formal email that should include

• subject,

• who you are,

• why you are writing the email,

• what would happen to your teacher and you,

• what you would do to solve it, and

• use *please let me know* appropriately.

• use *past participles as adjectives* appropriately.

GAPS

Genre		Audience	
Purpose		Style	

PREWRITING

DRAFT

FINAL DRAFT

CHECKLIST FOR REVISING AND EDITING

- Did I use the appropriate formal opening and closing? _____
- Did I use the appropriate formal letter structure? _____
- Did I keep English Letter Etiquette appropriately? _____
- Did I use *past participles* as adjectives? _____
- Did I use *please let me know-* appropriately? _____
- Did I understand the procedures of pre-writing, drafting, revising, and editing? _____

Summative Assessment: Writing Portfolio Assignment (WPA)

INDEPENDENT WRITING	The purpose of this task is for you to practice instruction writing.

You are writing a formal email that should include

• subject,

• who you are,

• why you are writing the email,

• what would happen to your teacher and you,

• what you would do to solve it, and

• use *please let me know* appropriately.

• use *past participles as adjectives* appropriately.

GAPS

Genre:		Audience:	
Purpose:		Style:	

PREWRITING

DRAFT

FINAL DRAFT

CHECKLIST FOR REVISING AND EDITING

- Did I use the appropriate formal opening and closing? _____
- Did I use the appropriate formal letter structure? _____
- Did I keep English Letter Etiquette appropriately? _____
- Did I use *past participles* as adjectives? _____
- Did I use *please let me know-* appropriately? _____
- Did I understand the procedures of pre-writing, drafting, revising, and editing? _____

FORMAL EMAIL RUBRIC FOR MODULE 8

BAND	GENRE FEATURES	COHERENCE AND COHESION	LEXICAL RESOURCE	GRAMMATICAL RANGE AND ACCURACY OF PAST VERBS, AND PAST PARTICIPLE	TASK ACHIEVEMENT
3	Correctly uses the typical structure of a formal email (e.g., opening, reasoning, etc.). Includes an appropriate subject and details with politeness.	Well-organized, with clear connections between sentences, and uses reasoning to help readers better understand.	Utilizes a simple range of vocabulary correctly and effectively, suitable for A1 level.	Uses basic grammatical structures, punctuation, *past verbs*, and *past participles* as adjectives, *please let me know* accurately and effectively, with no or very few errors.	Fully completes the task by appropriately addressing all aspects of the formal email writing prompt with simple yet accurate supporting ideas.
2	Partially includes a formal email genre feature with polite sentences, but some key elements may be missing or inadequately executed.	Generally well-organized but may lack some coherence in sentence connections or reasoning.	Uses some suitable vocabulary but may lack variety or contain some words not used correctly.	Uses some *past verbs*, and *past participles* as adjectives, and *please let me know* but may contain errors that sometimes obstruct understanding.	Partially completes the task by addressing some aspects of the prompt with a few relevant but simple supporting ideas; however, some aspects might be lacking.
1	Largely misses a formal email genre features, and includes inappropriate elements for an instruction.	Disorganized or lacks logical flow from one sentence to another.	Shows a lack of vocabulary variety or contains many words used incorrectly.	Lacks accuracy in the use of punctuation, *past verbs*, and *past participles* as adjectives, *please let me know* making the instruction difficult to understand.	Largely fails to address the formal email writing prompt appropriately or lacks the necessary supporting ideas.
0	The formal email is not written				

Formative Evaluation: Teachers' diaries and records

Name of student (grade in school)		
Date	Diary	Record

Summative Evaluation: Student Survey Questionnaire

	Rating scale questions	1 = "strongly disagree" 5 = "strongly agree"				
1	The goals of the course were clear and appropriate.	1	2	3	4	5
2	I was clearly stated my responsibilities and course requirements at the beginning.	1	2	3	4	5
3	The assessment used in the course was appropriate and fair.	1	2	3	4	5
4	The materials used in the course were appropriate and useful.	1	2	3	4	5
5	The texts and topics covered were interesting and relevant.	1	2	3	4	5
6	I was given clear instructions and explained things well.	1	2	3	4	5
7	I was given enough chances to write.	1	2	3	4	5
8	The lessons contained an appropriate variety of activities.	1	2	3	4	5
Open-ended questions						
9	What did you like most about the course?					
10	What did you like least about the course?					

Guided by Growth

1 This section provides a concise introduction to the key concepts and interrelations of TCL, genre writing, and process writing, which form the foundational methodology of this book. A thoughtful and thorough reading of this section is essential, as it will significantly benefit your understanding and participation in the class/

2 This document is a guide that provides a sample lesson plan to help teachers in their teaching process. Teachers don't have to follow it exactly, and it can be adjusted based on the teacher's experience and the needs of the students.

Using this guide could be very helpful for new teachers or those not very experienced with making lesson plans. It allows teachers to make their own lesson plans suitable for their students and their teaching situation.

This guide supports a detailed and effective way of planning lessons, making teachers more flexible and creative in their teaching strategies. This way, teaching becomes more focused on the students' needs, helping them learn in a way that's best for them.

3 Often, due to tight class schedules, instructors rush into lessons without clarifying the objectives. This lack of context is a key reason why students might not find the class engaging. By discussing questions and exchanging views with students, educators can leverage their existing knowledge and spark curiosity in the subject matter.

While many Korean English learners might not naturally choose to write diaries in English, I've included a diary module in this book for several reasons. Firstly, it's an excellent way to practice past tenses and improve coherence and cohesion. Many learners find it challenging to freely express their personal experiences and feelings in English, and the diary format can help break down these barriers. Plus, this module offers a chance to explore different ways of expressing time, rather than sticking to just one approach.

4 Learning keywords is a gradual process, not something that occurs instantly. A learner needs multiple exposures to a word to learn it effectively. The texts within a module generally reuse many of the words, facilitating this repetitive exposure. Additionally, there are more extensive learning resources available in the assignments towards the end of the book, which can be highly beneficial, so be sure to make good use of them. Most vocabulary learning focuses on linking words in Korean and English, but it's also crucial to remember the importance of learners consistently hearing the pronunciation and accent of essential words.

In this book, webtoons play a pivotal role in showcasing why this genre stands out uniquely. Instead of casually browsing through the webtoons, teachers should motivate learners by having them read in groups or participate in role-playing activities. Furthermore, guiding them through the webtoon dialogues will help them understand the essence of the genre and the book's overarching narrative

When introducing unfamiliar terms like "chain," students may feel intimidated. Encourage them to think of familiar examples in Korean, such as using different levels of politeness depending on the relationship. Once students grasp this concept, you can introduce "chain" in English by highlighting those similar concepts exist. Since many students are commonly aware that English lacks the concept of honorifics, discovering similarities with Korean may increase their interest in learning.

In Korea, most students are more likely to encounter situations where they email their subject teachers to submit assignments rather than emailing friends. Many students often include their name and grade/class in the email subject, but they need to learn the significance of the subject line to the reader and its function within the email. They should understand that the subject line should not be long; rather, as shown in good examples, it should include words relevant to the purpose of each email. By brainstorming various scenarios for sending emails and creating and comparing good and bad examples, students can better understand the dos and don'ts of effective email communication.

Emphasize to the students once again that there are expressions of honorifics in English as well. Since these expressions are mostly patterned, present various situations to the students so that they can apply the patterned honorific parts within the context.

It is anticipated that most students will find this part the most challenging. The necessity of this part lies in the fact that when writing, by the person who caused the problem proposing a solution first, it can make the recipient feel less burdened about finding a solution, through empathy with the recipient and offering solutions to conflict situations. Ultimately, it can be emphasized to the students through this part that communication is not solely about the transmission of information, but a means to win people's hearts through the exchange of emotions and to build better relationships from that.

Here, what we call "Common Sayings" are also widely recognized as "fixed expressions." Learning these as whole patterns, instead of dissecting their grammatical structures, can be more beneficial for learners. In the use of *please let me know,* learners often make mistakes because they use *will* with *if.* In such cases, explaining that will and if both carry the meaning of possibilities and thus they cannot be used at the same time, can be very helpful to learners.

Most students believe that there are no honorific expressions in English. However, this is a misconception. In English, formality is conveyed by creating a distance between the speaker and the listener through the use of tense, thereby elevating the listener within that distance. Therefore, 'could' is more polite than 'can'. While explaining this concept, let's help students understand that tense is not used solely for expressing time.

English verbs change in two ways: regularly and irregularly. Students need to understand this fundamental premise. For regular changes, convey the rules succinctly, and for irregular changes, let students know that although the verbs that change irregularly are fewer in number compared to verbs that change regularly, most of the commonly used verbs change irregularly. This reduces the students' burden while increasing the necessity to learn. In my case, rather than having students memorize the irregular three-form transformation of verbs by rote, on the assumption that they know the meaning of the base form, I first make them familiarize themselves with the sounds using chants. Also, since past participles make up the last part of the three-form transformation of verbs, they are often thought of as verbs. It is important to emphasize that these are not verbs but participles, which are derived from verbs and act as adjectives, and to emphasize that in Korean, they mean "되어진" to reduce confusion in future passive voice lessons.

[닫는 말]

Discover Writing Discover Korea 시리즈는 단순한 영어 학습서가 아닌, 한국 문화의 심장으로의 여행입니다. 이 시리즈 안에서 학습자들과 선생님들은 언어 학습과 문화적 몰입이 동시에 어우러진 독특한 경험을 할 수 있습니다. 일상 생활에서 먼 거리에 있던 그동안의 영어학습과 달리, 이 시리즈는 그 간극을 메워 교육적이면서도 공감 가능한 학습 경험을 제공합니다.

또한, 이 시리즈는 언어 학습에 새로운 시각을 제시합니다. 한국 문화, 관습 및 경험을 영어 교육에 엮음으로써 종합적인 접근 방식으로 언어를 습득할 기회를 제공합니다.

저는 여기에서 멈추지 않고 이 시리즈를 확장하고 한국 문화, 역사 및 현대 생활의 풍부함을 더 깊이 탐구하고 다른 장르로 확장할 계획이며 영어 쓰기교육을 넘어 읽기, 듣기 및 말하기를 포함한 종합적인 자료를 만들고 싶습니다.

흥미진진한 영어와 한국문화의 탐구 여정에 저와 함께 해보시면 어떨까요? 한 페이지 한 페이지마다 다양한 글의 장르와 한국을 탐험하면서 영어쓰기의 즐거움을 다시 발견해보세요. 독자가 되어 주심에 감사드리며, 앞으로의 만남을 기다리겠습니다.

2023 년 10 월 28 일

서은옥 드림

[Epilogue]

The **Discover Writing Discover Korea** series is not just a set of English textbooks; it's a journey into the heart of Korean culture. In these pages, you'll find a unique blend of language learning and cultural immersion. These books bridge the gap that feels distant from our daily lives, making the learning experience not only educational but also relatable.

It offers a fresh perspective on language learning. By weaving Korean culture, customs, and experiences into English education, it provides a holistic approach to language acquisition.

As for the future, my commitment is unwavering. I plan to expand this series, delving deeper into the richness of Korean culture, history, and modern life with other genres. I aim to create a comprehensive resource that not only enhances English writing skills but also reading listening and speaking, delving deeper into the richness of Korean culture, history, and modern life.

So, join me in this exciting journey of language and culture. Rediscover the joy of learning as you explore different genres and Korea, one page at a time. Thank you for your support, and I look forward to sharing more with you in the future.

Sincerely,

Eun-ok Seo

Discover Writing Discover Korea 8

발 행 | 2024년 8월 5일

저 자 | 서은옥

펴낸이 | 한건희

펴낸곳 | 주식회사 부크크

출판사등록 | 2014.07.15(제2014-16호)

주 소 | 서울특별시 금천구 가산디지털1로 119 SK트윈타워 A동 305호

전 화 | 1670-8316

이메일 | info@bookk.co.kr

ISBN | 979-11-410-9964-0

www.bookk.co.kr